# SPECIALS!

## SHAKESPEARE

*LIZ HARRIS*

## Romeo and Juliet

## David Orme

Folens Publishers

Editor: Catherine Miller
Layout artist: Suzanne Ward
Illustrations: Phil Hodgson
Cover:  Francesca Annis as Juliet and Ian McKellan as Romeo –
        The Shakespeare Centre Library (1976 Production)

First published 1995 by Folens Limited, Dunstable and Dublin.

ISBN 185276676-X      Printed in Singapore by Craft Print.

Folens Limited, Albert House, Apex Business Centre, Boscombe Road,
Dunstable, Beds LU5 4RL, England.

# Contents

Introduction                          4-5
Shakespeare's life and times           6
What is a play?                        7
Let's write a play 1                   8
Let's write a play 2                   9
Shakespeare's theatre                 10
A Shakespearian scene                 11
The missing page                      12
Tell the story                        13
A time line                           14
Who says?                             15
Headlines                             16
What scene?                           17
*Romeo and Juliet* today              18
New endings                           19
Character quiz                        20
Romeo                                 21
Juliet                                22
Mercutio                              23
The Nurse                             24
Character profile sheet               25
Minor characters                      26
Video watch                           27
Letters                               28
A diary                               29
Pardoned or punished?                 30
In the hot seat                       31
Guilty!                               32
Head to head                          33
Shakespeare's language                34
New words for old                     35
Pictures in words                     36
Performing Shakespeare                37
Performing a dialogue                 38
Performing speeches                   39
Performing a fight                    40
Young and old                         41
Themes from the play                  42
Loyalty                               43
Feuds                                 44
Tragedy                               45
Memorials                             46
Costumes                              47
In conclusion ...                     48

# Introduction

The study of Shakespeare offers both delights and difficulties for secondary pupils. Nevertheless, if it is presented in an appropriate way, all pupils can share in the richness of character and language.

The themes of *Romeo and Juliet* are not so far removed from the concerns of young people today: relationships with parents, authority, love and obedience.

The most appropriate way to present Shakespeare is as it was originally intended – as a live performance which can be followed by discussion. Pupils across the ability range are expected to engage with the play in some detail, both orally and in writing, and to demonstrate achievement in such areas as finding evidence, recognising themes, analysing character and tackling the language.

The greatest virtue of Shakespeare's plays is the language used. It is also often the most problematic area for pupils with special needs. The archaisms, the richness of allusion and imagery, the wit and concentration of language make Shakespeare a challenge for the most able pupils. If they apply themselves, all pupils can appreciate the unfolding story, identify characters and talk about themes and how they relate to their own lives. Real engagement with the text can baffle many, however. But it is this engagement that is required in the study of Shakespeare. It is not enough for a pupil to say, for example, that Tybalt is aggressive or bad tempered. We need them to substantiate statements with examples of his actions by references to the text.

The activities in this book provide a wide range of enjoyable tasks that are within the capabilities of most pupils. The issue of language and engagement with text has not been avoided and there is some specific work on Shakespeare's language. It is recognised that looking at the language, however simplified, is still difficult and these sheets may need to be tackled with a teacher, or by a small group with support.

It is assumed that pupils will have access to a video recording of the play and a play text.

**Video**

Seeing a live performance is, of course, an ideal introduction to the play but this is not always possible. In any case, video has other benefits:

– short sections can be used for language analysis
– pupils can see a scene more than once
– pupils can interrogate a particular scene
– pupils can focus on particular characters
– video can be paused for discussion and prediction of 'what happens next'.

Overall, it is probably best for the group to experience the whole play without interruption on the first occasion, if the timetable allows. Getting a feel for the sweep of play in this way will help pupils to overcome the initial confusion about what is happening and what the characters are talking about. Teachers may feel that, for some pupils, a synopsis of the play might help. This could provide a prompt as the play unfolds. A second viewing can be used for more detailed work. It is worthwhile for the teacher to view the video in advance and note the timings of various incidents, so that the whole tape does not need to be run in fast forward to find the scene being studied.

**Oral work**

The sheets require some of the work to be carried out in groups. These may consist of small groups within a mainstream class working with a support teacher, a whole class divided into a number of groups, or a small withdrawal group. The presence of, and monitoring by, a teacher or support teacher is essential for successful oral work. Four is a good number for a group, although some activities require three and some just two working in partnership. It is important that a sense of trust be built up within the groups.

1. *Discussion*. Simple discussion, both structured and unstructured is the best way of dealing with Shakespeare. If there are a number of groups within a class, a 'chair' may be asked to report back to the whole class, but this may be too formal for pupils with special needs. An exchange of group members is often more successful.

2. *Hot seating and role play*. These are valuable activities. Various hot-seating activities are presented and teachers and pupils can devise others. With role-playing games, opportunity is offered for some preparation in advance.

3. *Performance*. Three edited extracts from the play are offered – a speech, a dialogue and a fight scene. It is intended that these be developed into real theatre work, with pupils taking on the role of director. Clearly, the fight scene needs to be carefully controlled and choreographed. The focus should be on speaking the lines well. Although it may be too challenging to ask pupils to learn lines, they should at least know them reasonably well and feel confident in performing them. 'Reading round the class' is not an appropriate activity, and no pupil should be expected to read Shakespeare aloud without thorough preparation.

**Written work**

1. *Written work suggested by the play*. A range of structured writing tasks is offered that will develop understanding and be useful in their own right: diary writing, letter writing, scripting, using story boards and paraphrasing.

2. *Writing about the play*. The character sheets (pages 20–26) ask pupils to write directly about the play and supply evidence for the statements they make. These sheets can be used on an individual, groups or teacher–pupil basis.

**Knowledge about Shakespeare and drama**

The first activities build on and extend the pupil's own knowledge of Shakespeare, his theatre and scripting. It is important to understand the circumstances under which the plays were originally performed and how the text is written and translated into dialogue.

Teachers may find it useful to show how the plays are divided into acts and scenes and how the numbering of scenes works.

**Assessment**

Many activities contain an element of self-assessment and a more substantial assessment activity can be found on page 48.

Sharing Shakespeare with pupils presents the teacher with a unique opportunity, as this may well be one of the only opportunities that young people will have to enjoy these plays. If the pupil concludes that the academic work has spoiled the experience and that Shakespeare is not 'for them', then that would be, as Shakespeare himself might have described it, a 'most lamentable tragedy'.

# Shakespeare's life and times

● Research Shakespeare and his times. Fill in the gaps below.

Shakespeare was born in 15 _____.

He married Anne _____in
1580. They had three children.

Shakespeare moved to _____ in
1586. He became an actor and a writer.

His first plays were believed to be
*The Comedy* _____ (1592)
and *Titus* _____(1593).

Shakespeare's theatre was called the
_____. It was built in 1599.
It burned down in 1613.

Shakespeare wrote comedies such as
_____ and
_____. He also
wrote _____ such as *Romeo
and Juliet*, which was first performed in 1595.

In 1613 he retired to the town of his birth.

Important events during his lifetime were the
Spanish Armada in 15 _____, the
execution of Mary Queen of Scots in
15 _____ and the coming to the throne of
the new king, _____, in 1603.

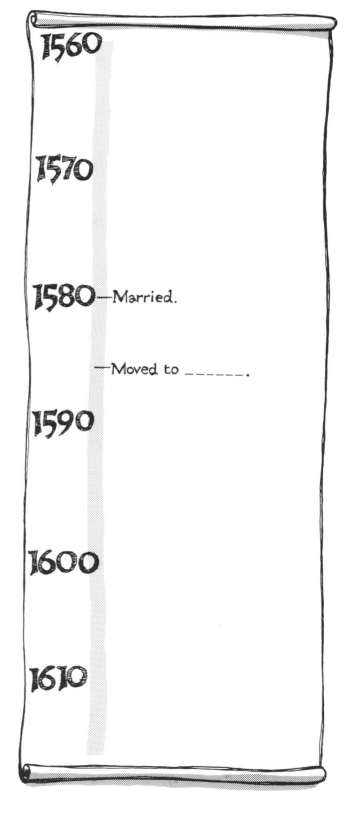

1560

1570

1580 —Married.

—Moved to _____.

1590

1600

1610

 ● Complete the time line.

*SPECIALS! Shakespeare Romeo and Juliet*                          © Folens

# What is a play?

- Below is a list of the things that might be different if the same story was made into a film, a television serial and a stage play.
- Complete the chart.

|  | Film | TV serial | Stage play |
|---|---|---|---|
| Setting |  |  | Only a few 'Sets' are possible |
| How long does it go on for? | Around two hours |  |  |
| What effects are possible? |  |  |  |
| Ending |  |  |  |
| Number of actors and extras. |  | Limited only by the budget |  |

- Here is a part of the script from *Romeo and Juliet*.
  Use the words on the right to label it correctly.

*Act Three, Scene One*

*A Street in Verona*          *Enter* TYBALT *and Others ...*

MERCUTIO: Good king of cats, nothing but one of your nine lives, that I mean to make bold withal, and, as you shall use me hereafter, dry-beat the rest of the eight. Will you pluck your sword out of his pilcher by the ears? Make haste, lest mine be about your ears ere it be out.       *(Draws.)*

                                          80

TYBALT: I am for you.
ROMEO: Gentle Mercutio, put thy rapier up.      *(They fight.)*
MERCUTIO: Come, sir, your passado.

Character speaking the lines.

Instruction to the actor or actress.

Line number.

Scene number.

Setting.

- Tick which of these people make use of the things you have labelled:

Actors ☐    Audience ☐    Director ☐    Scene painter ☐    You ☐

# Let's write a play - 1

A play needs characters, a place where it is set and an idea for a story.

- Here are some ideas to start off a play.
  Talk about them in groups and add to the ideas.

## Characters

Jane. 16 years old. Goes to St Monica's School. Lives with her mum and dad.

Brian. 17 years old. Goes to West Street School. Lives with his mum.

Jane's mum and dad.          Brian's mum.

Jane's friend Dianne.          More characters of your own ...

## Settings

Jane's house.

Brian's home.

The park.

The disco.

The shopping centre.

More settings of your own (overleaf) ...

## Story line

Jane and Brian are in love. Their families hate each other for something that happened in the past. They have forbidden the young people to see each other ...

_____

_____

_____

Continue over the page ...

- Write an outline of a story.

*SPECIALS! Shakespeare Romeo and Juliet*          © Folens

# Let's write a play - 2

● In your groups work out some characters, settings and a story idea for your own play.

## Characters

## Settings

**Ideas:**
animals?
teacher?
man?
woman?
villain?
heroine?
witch?
prince?
cowboy?

**Ideas:**
town?
house?
space?
school?
disco?
desert?
ranch?
jungle?
castle?

## Story line

_____

_____

_____

_____

**Ideas:**
romance?
horror?
adventure?
science fiction?
Western?
a mixture?
fable?

● Work together on a performance of a scene of your play.
● You could write a script or draw pictures.

# Shakespeare's theatre

● Label the diagram using the information below.

## Information box

**The tiring house** (behind the stage) – dressing rooms/storage area.
**The large stage**, which jutted out into the theatre.
**The trumpeter**, who told Londoners that the theatre was open.
**The galleries,** where those who had paid most sat.
**The groundlings**, people wo paid the least and stood to watch.
**The pit**, where the groundlings stood.

● Choose a scene from *Romeo and Juliet*.
How would you stage this play in Shakespeare's theatre?
● How would this staging be different from that found in a modern theatre?
Why?

*SPECIALS!* Shakespeare *Romeo and Juliet*                    © Folens

# A Shakespearean scene

● Choose a scene from *Romeo and Juliet*.
Draw what it might look like on an Elizabethan stage.

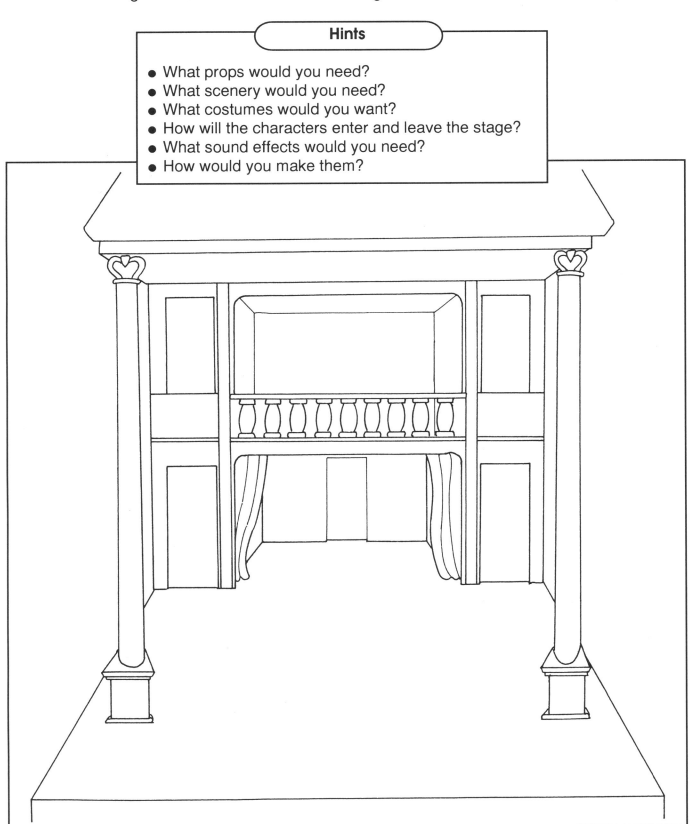

**Hints**

● What props would you need?
● What scenery would you need?
● What costumes would you want?
● How will the characters enter and leave the stage?
● What sound effects would you need?
● How would you make them?

# The missing page

● Complete the missing part of the story.

*In Verona two families, the Montagues and the Capulets, are enemies. Romeo, a Montague, and Juliet, a Capulet, fall in love. They secretly marry, although Juliet's parents have arranged a marriage between Juliet and Count Paris.*

*Romeo kills Tybalt, a Capulet, in a fight. He is sent away from Verona. What will happen to their love? Friar Lawrence, a friend of Romeo, thinks up a cunning plan to help them ...*

_____

_____

_____

_____

_____

_____

_____

*Juliet wakes up and finds Romeo dead. In her grief, she kills herself with Romeo's dagger.*

*The two families agree to become friends at last after the death of their children.*

SPECIALS! Shakespeare *Romeo and Juliet*

© Folens

# Tell the story

- Work in groups. Tell the story of *Romeo and Juliet* in turn.
- If the storyteller makes a mistake, the next person should start again at the beginning. Use the list of words and the pictures to help.

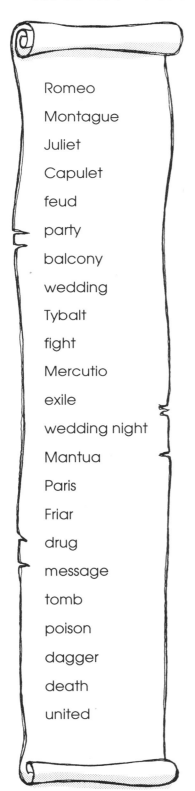

Romeo

Montague

Juliet

Capulet

feud

party

balcony

wedding

Tybalt

fight

Mercutio

exile

wedding night

Mantua

Paris

Friar

drug

message

tomb

poison

dagger

death

united

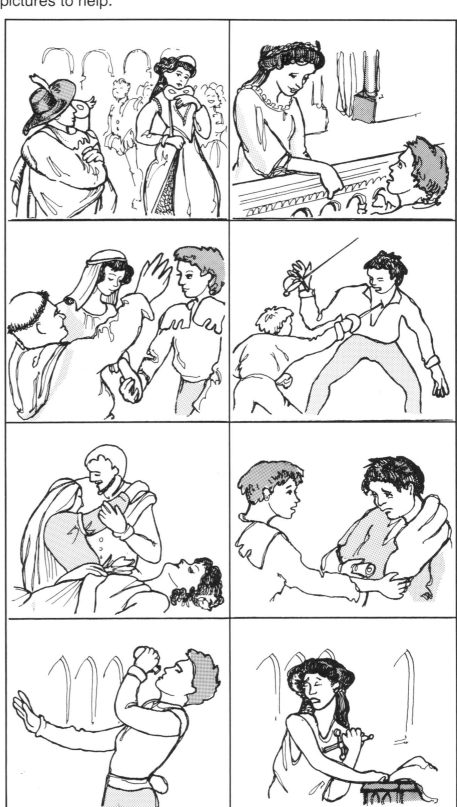

*SPECIALS!* Shakespeare *Romeo and Juliet*

# A time line

Follow the tragic story of *Romeo and Juliet*.
● Complete the time line by writing in the important events.

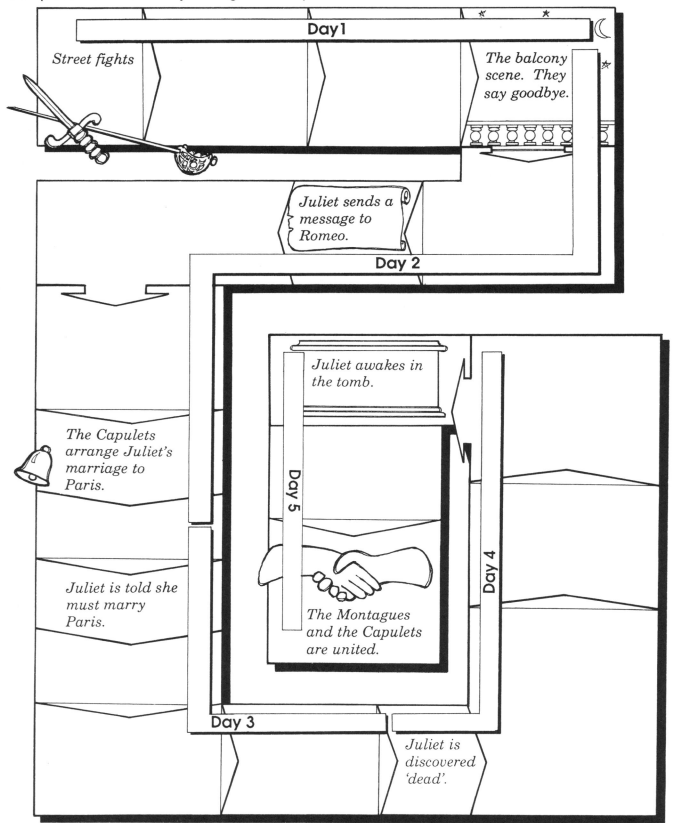

**Day 1**

*Street fights*

*The balcony scene. They say goodbye.*

*Juliet sends a message to Romeo.*

**Day 2**

*Juliet awakes in the tomb.*

*The Capulets arrange Juliet's marriage to Paris.*

**Day 5**

*Day 4*

*Juliet is told she must marry Paris.*

*The Montagues and the Capulets are united.*

**Day 3**

*Juliet is discovered 'dead'.*

# Who says?

● Find out who says these lines and to whom.

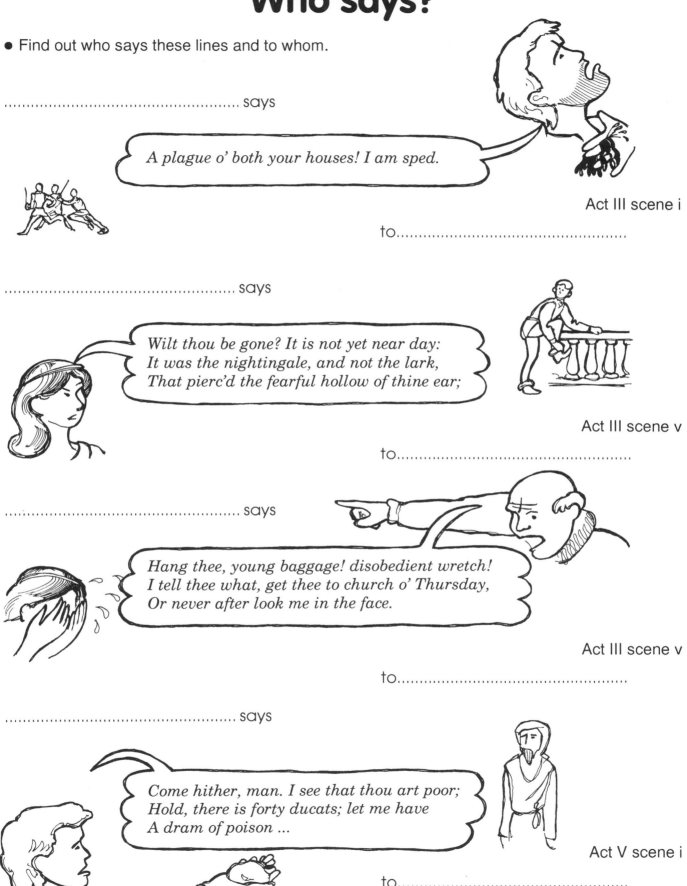

................................................. says

*A plague o' both your houses! I am sped.*

Act III scene i

to.................................................

................................................. says

*Wilt thou be gone? It is not yet near day:*
*It was the nightingale, and not the lark,*
*That pierc'd the fearful hollow of thine ear;*

Act III scene v

to.................................................

................................................. says

*Hang thee, young baggage! disobedient wretch!*
*I tell thee what, get thee to church o' Thursday,*
*Or never after look me in the face.*

Act III scene v

to.................................................

................................................. says

*Come hither, man. I see that thou art poor;*
*Hold, there is forty ducats; let me have*
*A dram of poison ...*

Act V scene i

to.................................................

# Headlines

Imagine what a newspaper would make of the events in *Romeo and Juliet*.
- Talk about the incidents that are described by the headlines below.
- In the space, write a headline of your own about a different incident.

- Write the newspaper story about one of the headlines.

*SPECIALS! Shakespeare Romeo and Juliet*     © Folens

# What scene?

- Put the scenes below in the correct order.
- There is an empty box for you to draw a scene you think is missing.

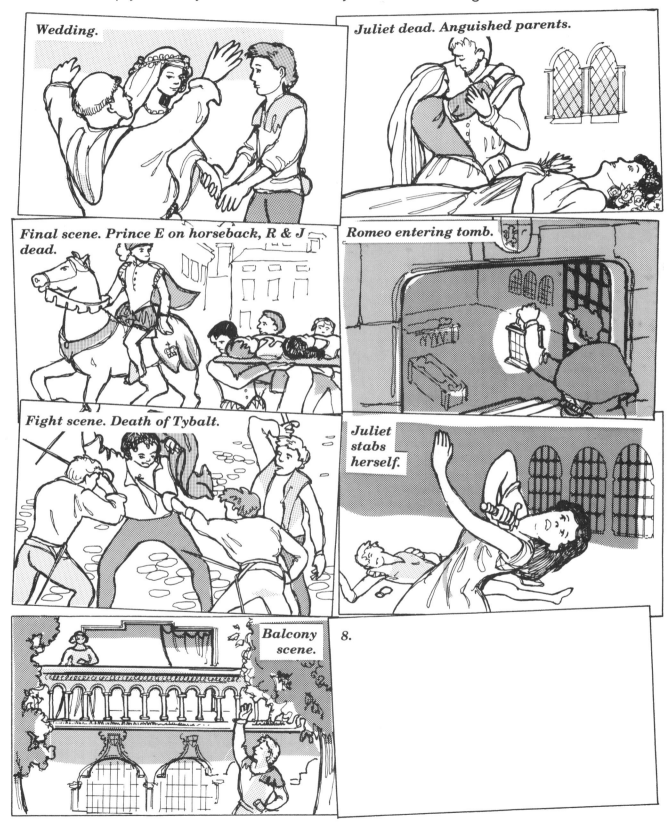

*Wedding.*

*Juliet dead. Anguished parents.*

*Final scene. Prince E on horseback, R & J dead.*

*Romeo entering tomb.*

*Fight scene. Death of Tybalt.*

*Juliet stabs herself.*

*Balcony scene.*

8.

# 'Romeo and Juliet' today

● Write a play based on *Romeo and Juliet*, set in the present day.
Here are some ideas:

*meet at pop concert*

*meet at school dance*

*meet on holiday*

*parents are rivals in business*

*boy and girl plan to run away*

*girl's father to arrange a change of school for her.*

{ A boy and girl who are in love. }

{ Parents who disapprove and try to keep them apart. }

| Characters | Setting |
|---|---|
|  |  |

MONTAGUE HOT DOGS    CAPULET'S BURGERS

## Story outline

1. _____

2. _____

3. _____

4. _____

5. _____

6. _____

● In groups, rehearse and perform your play.

# New endings

Some people do not like the ending of *Romeo and Juliet*.
They would rather have a happy one!
● Here are three alternative endings. Say which you prefer and why.
● Write about how the play might have continued.

**The story continues ...**

Romeo meets his old girlfriend, in Mantua. He decides that she was the one he loved after all.

Juliet wakes up just in time to stop Romeo drinking the poison. They make their escape.

Romeo is killed by Paris outside the tomb. Juliet is rescued from the tomb.

● Write your own ending. How would the story have developed?

### *Romeo and Juliet* – a new ending

_____

_____

_____

Continued over the page ...

# Character quiz

- The names of characters below are mixed up or missing. Work out their names and write them in the spaces.

*Rifar* ............................. friend of Romeo and Juliet.
(A *Rifar* is a type of monk).

Who is *Lituej's Snure?*

.................................................

*Count* ...................... is to have an arranged marriage with ...................

*Lord* ............................. and *Lady*
............................... Head of the *Catapule* family.

*Baltty*, short-tempered member of the
...................... family.

........................ 14-year-old daughter of *Capulet* and lady *Capulet*.

..............................., ruler of Verona

*Lord* ...................................... and *Lady*
...............................
Head of the *Gutmaneo* family.

*Bloonive*, nephew of Old *Gutmaneo* and friend of

...........................................

..............................., son of *Gutmaneo* and Lady *Gutmaneo*.

- Two families are mentioned in the play. Which of these servants work for each family? Complete the chart.

Peter
Sampson
Abraham
Potpan

Gregory
Balthasar
Anthony

| Family: | Family: |
|---|---|
|  |  |

*SPECIALS!* Shakespeare *Romeo and Juliet*  © Folens

# Romeo

● Write a character study of Romeo.

**What we find out**

**The evidence**

- - - - - - - - - - - - - - - - - - - - - - - - - - - - - - - - - - - - - - - - - -

*NOW*  ● Summarise what you have learned about Romeo.

_____

_____

_____

# Juliet

- Write a character study of Juliet.

**What we find out**

**The evidence**

- - - - - - - - - - - - - - - - - - - - - - - - - - - - - - - - - - - - - - - - - - - - - - - - - - - - -

*NOW*

- Summarise what you have learned about Juliet.

_____

_____

_____

*SPECIALS!* Shakespeare *Romeo and Juliet*   © Folens

# Mercutio

● Write a character study of Mercutio.

**What we find out**

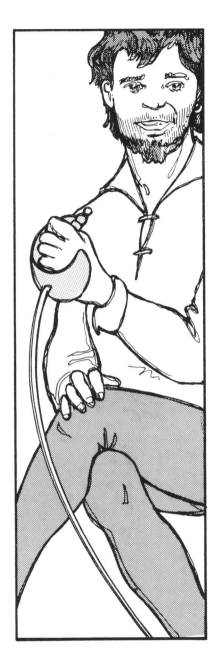

**The evidence**

● Summarise what you have learned about Mercutio.

_NOW_

_____

_____

_____

# The Nurse

● Write a character study of the Nurse.

**What we find out**

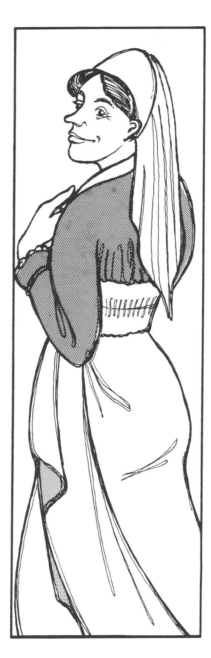

**The evidence**

- - - - - - - - - - - - - - - - - - - - - - - - - - - - - - - - - - - - - - - - - - -

*NOW*

● Summarise what you have learned about Juliet's Nurse.

_____

_____

_____

# Character profile sheet

● Use this sheet to help you write a character study.

Name of character: _____

**What we find out**

| What my character looks like | The evidence |
|---|---|
| | |

- - - - - - - - - - - - - - - - - - - - - - - - - - - - - - - - - - - - -

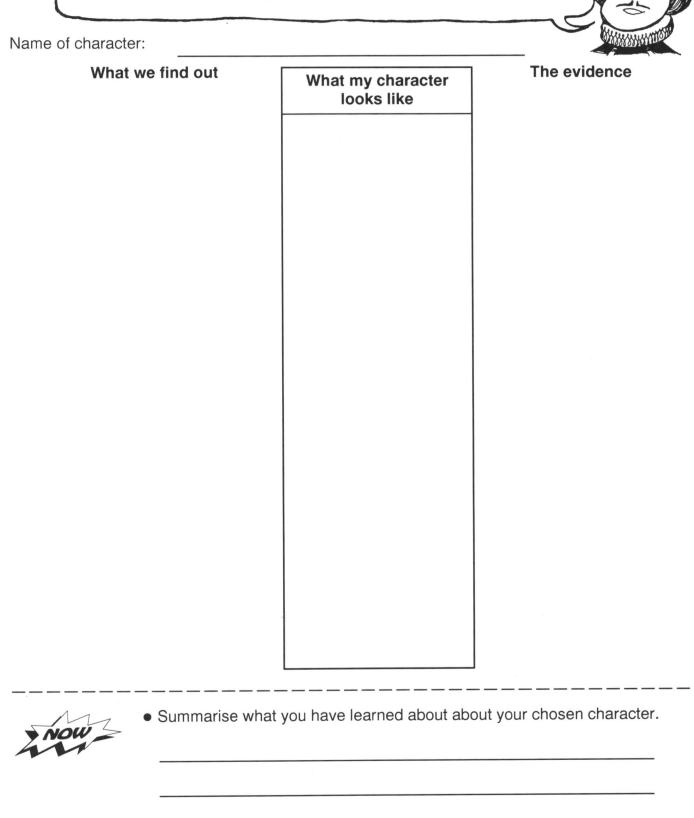

● Summarise what you have learned about about your chosen character.

_____

_____

# Minor characters

Use this page to record your impressions of some of the less important characters in *Romeo and Juliet*.

### *Rosaline*

Act I scene i, lines 202 to 222.

What sort of person is Rosaline?

_____

_____

What is said by her or about her?

_____

_____

_____

### *Count Paris*

Act I scene iii, lines 75 to 100.

What sort of person is Count Paris?

_____

_____

What is said by him or about him?

_____

_____

_____

### *Gregory and Sampson*

Act I scene i, lines 1 to 63.

What sort of people are Gregory and Sampson?

_____

_____

What is said by them or about them?

_____

_____

### *Prince Escalus*

Act I scene i, lines 79 to 101.

What sort of person is the Prince?

_____

_____

What is said by him or about him?

_____

_____

*SPECIALS! Shakespeare Romeo and Juliet*

© Folens

# Video watch

As you watch the video of *Romeo and Juliet,* make notes about a character. Use these boxes to help you.

**Name of character:** _____

What is the character like when he or she first appears?

Is the character talked about before he/she appears? What do others think of him/her?

What does the character look like?

What does the character say? What does it show about him/her?

What does the character think? How do you know this? What does it show about him or her?

How does the character act?

Are there times when the character surprises you in the way he or she acts? Why?

Does the character change? How? Why?

- Use your notes to write a full description of the character.
- Compare your version with someone else's. Are they different? In what ways?

# Letters

- Roll a dice and match the number against the names below to find who a letter is from.
- Roll again to find out who it is sent to.
  If both sender and receiver are the same person, roll again!

| Letter from | |
|---|---|
| 1 | Romeo |
| 2 | Juliet |
| 3 | Lord Capulet |
| 4 | Tybalt |
| 5 | Nurse |
| 6 | Friar Lawrence |

| Letter to | |
|---|---|
| 1 | Juliet |
| 2 | Romeo |
| 3 | Lady Montague |
| 4 | Mercutio |
| 5 | Friar Lawrence |
| 6 | Lord Paris |

- What would they want to say to the person they are writing to?
- At what point in the play are they writing the letter?

*From:* _____

*To:* _____

Continue over the page ...

- Now pass your letter on to a partner. Ask them to write a reply.

*SPECIALS! Shakespeare Romeo and Juliet* © Folens

# A diary

- Make the spinner below and use it to find a diary-writer.

| Diary writer | |
|---|---|
| 1 | *Romeo* |
| 2 | *Juliet* |
| 3 | *Mercutio* |
| 4 | *Tybalt* |
| 5 | *Nurse* |
| 6 | *Friar Lawrence* |

Think about:
- What point in the play you want to write the diary entry about.
- How the person is feeling about events taking place.
- What action the person will take.

Cut and paste on to card. Push a stick through the centre. Spin it.

**NOW**

- Write the diary entry.

Day: _____

Date: _____

# Pardoned or punished?

At the end of the play, the Prince says:

*Some shall be pardoned, and some punished.*

Imagine you are one of these characters:

**The Nurse**　　　　**Friar Lawrence**　　　　**Lord Montague**　　　　**Lord Capulet**

- You are about to be interviewed by the Prince. You do not want to be punished.
- Make notes about what you did in the play that would help you defend yourself.

### NOTES

Continue over the page ...

- You are allowed to defend yourself for two minutes. Your group will then decide whether you are to be pardoned or punished!

# In the hot seat

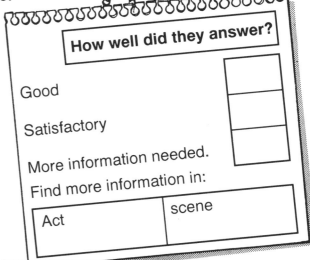

ye hot stool

- Work in groups. Each person should choose a character from *Romeo and Juliet.*
- Write three questions to ask someone in that role.
- When they have answered, give them your response.

1. _____

   _____

   _____

   - Have you learned anything new about the character?

| How well did they answer? | | |
|---|---|---|
| Good | | |
| Satisfactory | | |
| More information needed. | | |
| Find more information in: | | |
| Act | scene | |

2. _____

   _____

   _____

   - Have you learned anything new about the character?

| How well did they answer? | | |
|---|---|---|
| Good | | |
| Satisfactory | | |
| More information needed. | | |
| Find more information in: | | |
| Act | scene | |

3. _____

   _____

   _____

   - Have you learned anything new about the character?

| How well did they answer? | | |
|---|---|---|
| Good | | |
| Satisfactory | | |
| More information needed. | | |
| Find more information in: | | |
| Act | scene | |

# Guilty!

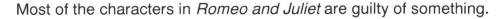

Order in court!

Most of the characters in *Romeo and Juliet* are guilty of something.

Juliet is guilty of marrying against her parents' will.

Tybalt and Romeo are guilty of murder.

- Work in pairs. Talk about the events of the play and complete the list below. If you didn't agree, say why.

| |
|---|
| Capulet and Montague are guilty of ...<br><br>We disagreed about ... |
| The Nurse is guilty of ...<br><br>We disagreed about ... |
| Friar Lawrence is guilty of ...<br><br>We disagreed about ... |

- Choose a character to be put on trial.
  - Someone will have to defend the character.
  - Someone will have to prosecute.
  - You will need a judge to keep order.

# Head to head

- Work in threes. Two of you need to make and use the dice to see which characters you have become. (Roll again if you both get the same character.)
- Improvise a conversation between the two characters.
- The third person should fill in the assessment card.

**1** Lord Capulet
**2** Friar Laurence
**3** Lord Montague
**4** Tybalt
**5** Mercutio
**6** The Nurse

### Assessment card

Name _____

What character did he/she play? _____

How well did he/she improvise the characters? _____

_____

Name _____

What character did he/she play? _____

How well did he/she improvise the characters? _____

_____

# Shakespeare's language

Shakespeare's language can be difficult. Remember:

| | |
|---|---|
| Shakespeare was writing poetry and poetry always needs to be listened to carefully. | Shakespeare was writing 400 years ago and language has changed since then. |

- Work in pairs.  Read the passage below from Act I scene v.

  - Mark in **GREEN** any words you do not know.

  - Mark in **RED** any words that seem to be old fashioned.

  - Mark in **BLUE** any words that seem to have a different meaning to the same word today.

  - Mark in **YELLOW** any sections where Romeo compares Juliet to something.

**Romeo**

O! she doth teach the torches to burn bright.

It seems she hangs upon the cheek of night

Like a rich jewel in an Ethiop's ear;

Beauty too rich for use, for earth too dear!

So shows a snowy dove trooping with crows,

As yonder lady o'er her fellows shows.

The measure done, I'll watch her place of stand,

And, touching hers, make blessed my rude hand.

Did my heart love till now? Forswear it, sight!

For I ne'er saw true beauty till this night.

- Compare your results with people from another group.
  Use your text notes to find the meaning of any difficult or strange words.
- Why does Romeo compare Juliet to so many things?

# New words for old

Many words have changed their meanings over the last 400 years.

But now, my Lord, what say you to my suit?

- Talk about the words highlighted in the speeches below.
  Your text notes might help you to find their meanings in the play.
- What do they mean today? Find a modern substitute.

*Romeo about Juliet (Act I scene v)*

And touching hers, make blessed my **rude** hand.

*Capulet to Tybalt (Act I scene v)*

You are a **saucy** boy.

*Sampson to Gregory when they meet the Capulets (Act I scene i)*

I will frown as I pass by, and let them take it as they **list**.

*Paris to Capulet (Act I scene ii)*

But now, my Lord, what say you to my **suit**?

*Romeo in the tomb (Act V scene iii)*

The dashing rocks thy sea-sick weary **bark**!

*Friar Lawrence to Romeo (Act II scene iii)*

Be plain, good son, and **homely** in thy **drift**.

- Write a sentence using some of these words as Shakespeare understood them.

_____

_____

# Pictures in words

Shakespeare's descriptions are full of comparisons.

● Work with a partner. Can you explain these three examples?

| Lady Capulet describes Paris as a book. | Juliet wants time to pass by quickly like galloping horses. | Romeo says Juliet is like a white dove. |
| --- | --- | --- |
| Read o'er the volume of young Paris's face, And find delight writ there with beauty's pen. | Gallop apace, you fiery footed steeds ... | So shows a snowy dove trooping with crows As yonder lady o'er her fellows shows. |

● Talk about the word-pictures in the scene below, Act I scene iv.
● Why are there so many comparisons to Cupid? Underline them in red.
● Underline in blue any other comparisons to do with love.
● Can you find any jokes?

| | |
| --- | --- |
| *Romeo* | Give me a torch: I am not for this ambling; Being but heavy, I will bear the light. |
| *Mercutio* | Nay, gentle Romeo, we must have you dance. |
| *Romeo* | Not I, believe me: you have dancing shoes With nimble soles; I have a soul of lead So stakes me to the ground I cannot move. |
| *Mercutio* | You are a lover; borrow Cupid's wings, And soar with them above a common bound. |
| *Romeo* | I am too sore enpierced with his shaft To soar with his light feathers; and so bound I cannot bound a pitch above dull woe: Under love's heavy burden do I sink. |
| *Mercutio* | And, to sink in it, should you burden love; Too great oppression for a tender thing. |
| *Romeo* | Is love a tender thing? it is too rough, Too rude, too boisterous; and it pricks like thorn. |

# Performing Shakespeare

- Work together in groups of five on the scene below (Act I scene i).
  Four people should play the parts, while the fifth should act as director.
  'Biting your thumb' at someone was considered a very rude gesture!

**The words**. You do not need to learn them, but make sure you have practised them thoroughly.

**Expression**. Talk about what sort of characters the servants have. What are they trying to do? In your performance, try and give each one a character of his own.

**Think about:**

**Movement**. Use the space you have available effectively. The director needs to organise this. In this scene there is almost a fight. How will this be staged?

*Enter ABRAHAM and another MONTAGUE servant ...*

| | |
|---|---|
| **GREGORY** | Here comes two of the house of the Montagues. |
| **SAMSON** | My naked weapon is out; quarrel, I will back thee. |
| **GREGORY** | How! Turn thy back and run? |
| **SAMSON** | Fear me not. |
| **GREGORY** | No, marry; I fear thee! |
| **SAMSON** | Let us take the law of our sides; let them begin. |
| **GREGORY** | I will frown as I pass by, and let them take it as they list. |
| **SAMSON** | I will bite my thumb at them; which is a disgrace to them, if they bear it. |

*(He bites his thumb)*

| | |
|---|---|
| **ARBRAHAM** | Do you bite your thumb at us, sir? |
| **SAMSON** | *(To ABRAHAM)* No sir, I do not bite my thumb at you sir, but I bite my thumb, sir. |
| **GREGORY** | *(To ABRAHAM)* Do you quarrel, sir? |
| **ABRAHAM** | Quarrel, sir! no, sir. |
| **SAMSON** | If you do sir, I am for you: I serve as good a man as you. |
| **ABRAHAM** | No better. |
| **SAMSON** | Well, sir.                              *(Enter BENVOLIO)* |
| **GREGORY** | Say 'better'; here comes one of my master's kinsmen. |
| **SAMSON** | *(To ABRAHAM)* Yes, better, sir. |
| **ABRAHAM** | You lie. |
| **SAMSON** | Draw, if you be men! |
| **BENVOLIO.** | Part, fools! Put up your swords; you know not what you do! |

- Work in larger groups to continue the scene, up to the point where the Prince enters.

# Performing a dialogue

Romeo and Juliet have to part after spending their first night together.

- Work with a partner on a performance of the dialogue below from Act III scene v.
- Use your text to find out meanings of words you do not know.

> **Some help**
>
> A nightingale is a bird that sings at night.
> A lark sings early in the morning and tells
> us that dawn has broken.

**JULIET**    Wilt thou be gone? it is not yet near day:
It was the nightingale, and not the lark,
That pierc'd the fearful hollow of thine ear;
Nightly she sings on yon pomegranate tree:
Believe me, love, it was the nightingale.

**ROMEO**    It was the lark, the herald of the morn,
No nightingale: look, love, what envious streaks
Do lace the severing clouds in yonder east:
Night's candles are burnt out, and jocund day
Stands tiptoe on the misty mountain tops:
I must be gone and live, or stay and die.

**JULIET**    Yon light is not daylight, I know it, I:
It is some meteor that the sun exhales,
To be to thee this night a torch-bearer
And light thee on thy way to Mantua:
Therefore stay yet; thou need'st not to be gone.

**ROMEO**    Let me be taken, let me be put to death;
I am content, so thou wilt have it so ...
... I have more care to stay than will to go:
Come death, and welcome! Juliet wills it so.
How is't, my soul? let's talk. It is not day.

**JULIET**    It is, it is; hie hence, be gone, away!
It is the lark that sings so out of tune,
Straining harsh discords and unpleasing sharps ...
... O! now be gone; more light and light it grows.

- Talk about what problems you would face as director of this scene.
- Would Shakespeare have faced the same problems?

# Performing speeches

- Practise these two speeches with a partner.
  Divide the speeches up so you say one half each.
  Think carefully about what you know of the character and the situation.
  This will decide your expression.

*FROM ACT 4*
### The Nurse discovers that Juliet is 'dead'

**NURSE:** Mistress! what, mistress! Juliet! fast, I warrant her, she:
Why, lamb! Why lady! fie you slug-a-bed!
Why, love, I say! madam! sweet-heart! why, bride!
What! not a word? you take your pennyworths now:
Sleep for a week for the next night, I warrant,
The County Paris hath set up his rest
That you shall rest but little. God forgive me,
Marry, and amen, how sound is she asleep!
I needs must wake her. Madam, madam, madam!
... What, dress'd! and in your clothes! and down again!
I must needs wake you. Lady! lady! lady!
Alas! alas! Help! help! my lady's dead!
O! well-a-day that ever I was born.
Some *aqua-vitae*, ho! My lord! my lady!

*FROM ACT 3*
### Mercutio speaks to Benvolio

**MERCUTIO:** Thou! why, thou wilt quarrel with a man
that hath a hair more or a hair less in his beard than
thou hast. Thou wilt quarrel with a man for cracking
nuts, having no other reason but because thou hast
hazel eyes. What eye, but such an eye would spy out
such a quarrel? Thy head is as full of quarrels as an egg
is full of meat, and yet thy head hath been beaten as
addle as an egg for quarrelling. Thou hast quarrelled
with a man for coughing in the street, because he hath
wakened thy dog that hath lain asleep in the sun ... And
yet thou wilt tutor me from quarrelling!

*NOW* • Perform your speeches.

# Performing a fight

Tybalt is looking for Romeo, to fight him. Romeo will not fight because he is related to Tybalt since he married Juliet. Tybalt does not know this.

- Rehearse this scene in groups (Act III scene i).
  **SAFETY** is very important when rehearsing fight scenes.
  Mime the actions first. Remember, actors do not really fight on stage.

| | |
|---|---|
| **TYBALT** | *(To ROMEO)* ... turn and draw. |
| **ROMEO** | I do protest I never injur'd thee, |
| | But love thee better than thou canst devise, |
| | Till thou shalt know the reason of my love ... |
| **MERCUTIO** | *(Drawing his sword)* |
| | O calm, dishonorable, vile submission! ... |
| | ... Tybalt, you ratcatcher, will you walk? |
| **TYBALT** | What wouldst thou have with me? |
| **MERCUTIO** | Good king of cats, nothing but one of your nine lives ... |
| | ... Will you pluck your sword out of his pilcher by the ears? |
| | make haste, lest mine be about your ears ere it be out. |
| **TYBALT** | *(Drawing his sword)* I am for you. |
| **ROMEO** | Gentle Mercutio, put thy rapier up. |
| **MERCUTIO** | Come sir, your passado. |

*(They fight)*

| | |
|---|---|
| **ROMEO** | *(Drawing his sword)* |
| | Draw, Benvolio; beat down their weapons. |
| | Gentlemen, for shame, forbear this outrage! |
| | Tybalt, Mercutio, the prince expressly hath |
| | Forbidden bandying in Verona streets. |
| | Hold Tybalt! good Mercutio! |

*(ROMEO beats down their swords and rushes between them. TYBALT under ROMEO'S arm thrusts at MERCUTIO.)*

| | |
|---|---|
| **MERCUTIO** | I am hurt? A plague o' both your houses! |

 • Perform your scene.

40  *SPECIALS! Shakespeare Romeo and Juliet*  © Folens

# Young and old

In *Romeo and Juliet*, there are times when
young people and older people are in conflict.

● Can you think of examples?

*When?* _____

*Why?* _____

*Quotation to
prove my point* _____

_____


*When?* _____

*Why?* _____

*Quotation to
prove my point* _____

_____


**NOW** ● Sometimes in the play, the old and young understand each other
better and work together. Can you think of an example?

*When* _____

Continue over the page ...

# Themes from the play

- A play has characters and action, but it also has a theme. The theme of a play is the same as the subject, so *Romeo and Juliet* obviously has the theme of love. How many other themes can you find in the wordsearch?

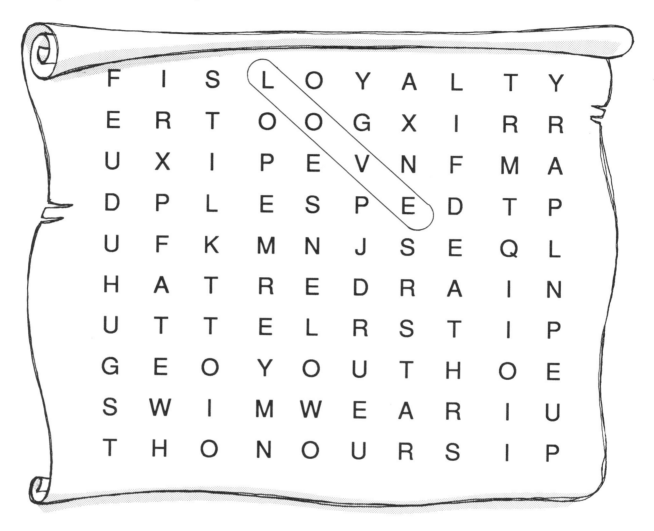

```
F I S L O Y A L T Y
E R T O O G X I R R
U X I P E V N F M A
D P L E S P E D T P
U F K M N J S E Q L
H A T R E D R A I N
U T T E L R S T I P
G E O Y O U T H O E
S W I M W E A R I U
T H O N O U R S I P
```

- Write them below.

_____      _____

_____      _____

_____      _____

- Turn over and make a list of the characters you associate with these themes. Explain your choice.

# Loyalty

There are many examples of loyalty in *Romeo and Juliet.*

● Complete the chart. Can you find other examples?

| Who is loyal? | How? | Evidence from the play |
|---|---|---|
| Juliet is loyal to Romeo, even though he has killed Tybalt. | | |
| Romeo is loyal to his friend Mercutio. | | |
| The Nurse is loyal to Juliet. | | |
| The Capulets and Montagues are loyal to their own families even if it means killing. | | |
| | | |

**NOW** ● Talk in groups about when loyalty is right and when it is not such a good idea. Complete the sentences below.

I am loyal when _____

I am not loyal when _____

# Feuds

What is a feud?

- Work in pairs. Talk about the words below and decide the differences between them.

row    argument    fight    feud    hatred

- Which of these lines come from a story about a feud?

**1**
" I hate our teacher. He's always picking on me."

**2**
"We have a match against Gas St School every year and it's great when we beat them."

**3**
"The Dimheads gang has been fighting with the Plonks for years."

**4**
"You can't go out with him. He's too old for you."

**5**
"I hate her and I always will."

**NOW**

- In *Romeo and Juliet*, the Montagues and Capulets are involved in a feud. Write down any evidence you can find for this. What is the result of their feud?

**Feuds in 'Romeo and Juliet'**

# Tragedy

*Romeo and Juliet* is a tragedy.

- Today, newspapers and the television call anything that is sad, a tragedy.

"CLOSING THIS HOSPITAL IS A TRAGEDY," SAYS DR.

Tragic death of actor CAR CRASH VICTIM AGED JUST 42.

PLANE CRASH TRAGEDY DEATH TOLL RISES

Sometimes, it is a big disaster.

- Shakespeare would have wanted a few more things included before he would call a story a tragedy.

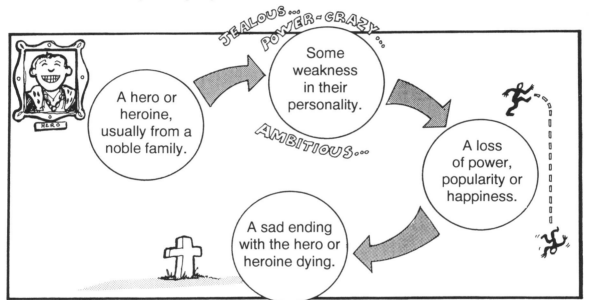

JEALOUS... POWER-CRAZY... AMBITIOUS...

A hero or heroine, usually from a noble family.

Some weakness in their personality.

A loss of power, popularity or happiness.

A sad ending with the hero or heroine dying.

NOW

- Look at the stories and headlines below.
  Which are tragedies in the modern sense?
- Which are tragedies as Shakespeare would have understood them?
  Which are not tragedies at all?

Daughter of judge dies after drug overdose.

Too late to save boy stuck in landslide.

Dog goes missing.

Prince kills himself after losing palace in gambling party.

Forty dead after hotel fire.

# Memorials

● Here are memorials to the four people who die in *Romeo and Juliet*.
  What would you write on them?

**Hints**

- Who were they?
- Which family did they belong to?
- Who were their parents?
- When did they die?
- Where did they die?
- How did they die?
- Why did they die?
- How can you summarise their characters?

ROMEO

Juliet

Mercutio

Tybalt

# Costumes

*Romeo and Juliet* could be set at any time – past, present or future and in almost any setting. The musical *West Side Story* is based on *Romeo and Juliet* and is set in New York in the 1950s.

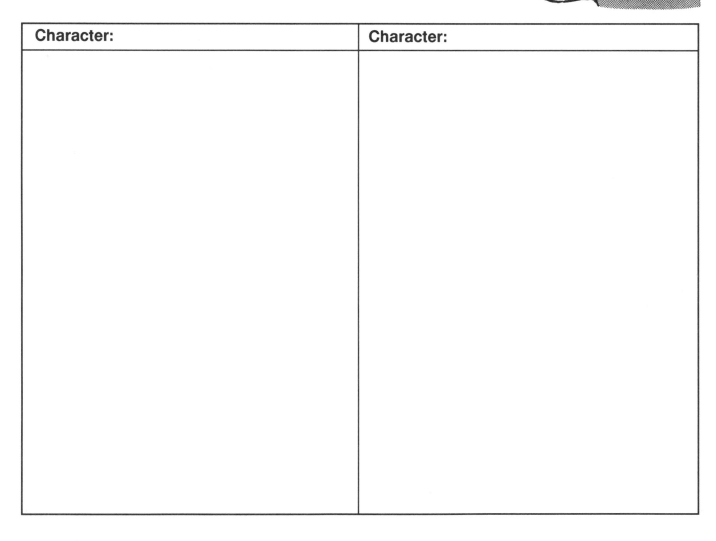

- Complete the sentences and design costumes for two characters.

**When?  The performance is set ...**

_____

**Where? The performance is set ...**

_____

| Character: | Character: |
|---|---|
|  |  |

- Compare your designs with someone else.
  Explain any differences.

© Folens                                    *SPECIALS!* Shakespeare *Romeo and Juliet*                                    47

# In conclusion ...

- When you watched the play, how easy was it to follow the story?

easy ☐   fairly easy ☐   difficult ☐   easier than reading the play ☐   harder than working on the play in class ☐

- What made it difficult to follow the story?

language? ☐   plot too complicated? ☐   not interesting enough? ☐

- List the activities you have finished and complete the chart.

| Activity | How well you did | Problems |
|---|---|---|
| | | |

- Which aspect of studying the play did you find the most difficult?
- What have you achieved from studying *Romeo and Juliet*?

*SPECIALS! Shakespeare Romeo and Juliet*   © Folens